FOR ROBIN RICHARDSON,
CREATIVE SPIRIT AND STORY-TELLER OF THE WORLD

....

I would like to thank the following friends, colleagues and family members
for their help in writing this book:
Paul Alford, Mashuq ibn Ally, Margaret Engler, Ester Gluck, Rabbi Hugo Gryn, Catherine Grigg,
Judith Grigg, Ron Maddox and colleagues at The Buddhist Society, Dr Gamal Solaiman,
Sharada Sugirtharajah and Swami Tripurananda.

....

This anthology has been inspired by *Quest*,
the series of religious education programmes for 7–11 year olds
broadcast on Channel 4 Schools.

Quest: Creation Stories was produced by Tern Television for Channel 4 Schools.

Published by The Educational Television Company Ltd
Leah House
10a Great Titchfield Street
London W1P 7AA

Written by Angela Wood
Illustrated by Sue Clarke
Designed by Andrew Barron & Collis Clements Associates
Typeset in Monotype Perpetua
Printed in Great Britain by Bath Press Colourbooks, Glasgow

ISBN 1-899214-50-X

CREATION STORIES
ANTHOLOGY

NOTES

The Christian creation 'story' is two stories joined together, at the very beginning of the Bible, the holy book of Christianity. The stories were written at different times, with different ideas about creation. They were written in Hebrew and were part of the Jewish Bible at first and then also the Christian Bible.

Hebrew has a special word for God creating the universe. There is a different word for creating by, say, a cook or an artist. But the special Hebrew word shows that the way God 'creates' is very different from the way that people 'create'.

The first story was written as a song that the ancient Jews sang in the temple. The song was a prayer thanking God for creating a beautiful world. That is why the story is set out in verses and some phrases keep coming back, a bit like a chorus.

For Jews and Christians, the story is about who created the world and why – not about how. Some may accept that our universe has developed over billions of years but that does not change their belief in God. Others believe that the universe was created in six days, as in the story.

CHRISTIANITY

Nothing and Everything

Nothing. Nothing to see. Nothing to hear. Nothing to touch. Nothing to taste. Nothing to smell. Just nothing.

But God. Not seeing. Not hearing. Not touching. Not tasting. Not smelling. Just being.

And from being, God makes everything. The sky, the earth, the water. Everything.

The earth is totally empty and the water is totally dark but the Spirit of God sweeps across the water.

Light appears, to give life. Light and darkness drift apart as they do every day when day turns to night and night turns to day. This evening and this morning make the first day.

A huge space appears in the middle of the water and the water runs above it and below it. The water below becomes the sea and the water above becomes the sky that carries rain. This evening and this morning make a second day.

The waters below the sky come together so that dry land appears, the earth where we live. All kinds of plants sprout on the earth – luscious fruit trees, fragrant flowers, waving ears of corn… This evening and this morning make a third day.

Lights appear in the sky, separating day and night, and marking days and years. And then two great light-givers. The bigger light, the sun, shines in the day and the smaller light, the moon, shines at night. Stars also appear. This evening and this morning make a fourth day.

Some of the main ideas in the story are:

★ God created the universe for a reason
★ the universe is created perfectly
★ men and women ('man') are created together
★ they are created 'in God's image'
★ they are created last, when everything else is in place

The story tells of rest created on the seventh day because of the Jewish Sabbath, the rest day from Friday evening to Saturday evening. It is a time of peace and happiness. Early Christians changed the Sabbath to Sunday, because they believe that God's son, Jesus Christ, rose from the dead on a Sunday after dying on a Friday.

In the story, heaven is like an actual place – 'up there'. For centuries, Christian artists have shown heaven like the sky. Many Christians think of heaven as 'above' and talk about 'going up to heaven'. The Bible supports this by explaining that this is what Jesus Christ did after his death.

The first story has a 'ladder' of creation: after the basic creation of the universe, there are plants, then animals and finally people, as if everything was preparing for people and was created for them. It says that people are 'in the image of God', not because people 'look like' God but they are 'like' God in some ways and are open to God's blessing.

All kinds of creatures appear in the sky and the sea – birds and insects, fish and reptiles… They spread across the sky and the sea and more and more of them appear until the sky and sea fill up with them. This evening and this morning make a fifth day.

All kinds of animals appear on the earth – lions and bears, cattle and sheep, squirrels and rats… Then come the people, on the same day. They are like the other animals in so many ways but like God, too. The people have God's image in them and are filled with God's blessing. They spread and grow. They are given all the birds, fish and animals. They are in charge of them and need to care for them. And, for God, this is all very good. This evening and this morning make a sixth day.

Now there is light and darkness, sky, earth and sea, plants and trees, fishes and birds, animals and people. There is just one more thing that the world needs for creation to be complete – peaceful rest. It is a special day, the seventh day, and God blesses it and makes it holy.

NOTES

When the second story begins, the universe is already 'there'. Man is created and then woman from man. There is a Jewish saying that many Christians like to use which goes: 'Woman was not created from man's foot so that he should stand over her and not from his head so that she should stand over him. She was created from his rib, near his heart, so that they should love each other.'

Some Christians believe that, because Adam and Eve disobeyed God, they 'fell' from the important place they had. They also believe that everyone descended from Adam and Eve and so everyone is 'fallen'. This is called 'Original Sin'. Many Christians believe that babies are born in a state of sin and baptise them to make the baby's life new again.

The story answers many questions about life... Why are men and women different and the same? Why can't we have and know everything? Why do women have pain in childbirth? Why do we dream of something perfect? Why do we feel we are like God but also not like God?

CHRISTIANITY

The Garden and the Gates

The world is ready and Adam is created. He and the earth belong together. He comes from dust with God's breath to give him life, and finds himself in a garden filled with everything. Everything. Everything to see. Everything to hear. Everything to touch. Everything to taste. Everything to smell. In the middle is the tree of life, that tells good and bad.

Adam hears God saying that he is free to use the garden and that he can eat all but one fruit… If he eats from the tree that tells good and bad, life will never be the same and he will not live for ever.

Animals appear in the garden and Adam gives them names. But they are not like him and he needs a special partner. God makes Adam fall asleep and uses a rib from his body to create a woman. Adam says, 'This woman is bone of my bones and flesh of my flesh. We are one.'

The woman hears a snake saying, 'Surely there aren't fruits you shouldn't eat…'

She replies, 'We can eat any fruit except from the tree that tells good and bad. If we do, life will never be the same and we won't live for ever.'

'You won't die from a fruit! It's just that God doesn't want you to know everything…'

She wonders: shouldn't we know good and bad, if they're part of life? She plucks a fruit and bites hard. 'This tastes good!' Adam takes the bite she offers.

Many Christians and Jews today do not believe that Adam and Eve were actual people. Rather they think that this story shows that we all choose to do wrong things sometimes.

Christians believe that God sent Jesus into the world to change people for the better and save the world from sin by bringing people back to God. Some Christians describe Christ as the 'Second Adam' and his mother, Mary, as the 'Second Eve'.

The Adam and Eve story has been a favourite subject for western artists for centuries and often appears in advertising. Sometimes artists and film makers add their own images to the story. Often, the fruit is an 'apple', usually Eve is shown as very sexy and sometimes the snake is portrayed as a demon.

In all the stories and pictures based on this creation story, the garden of Eden is an image of heaven and a perfect place where everyone would like to be or to return.

A new world opens up and they see each other differently. They know they are naked and feel they must cover their bodies. It was true… life will never be the same.

They hear God call, 'Where are you?'

Doesn't God know where I am, the man wonders. But do I know where I am and who I am now? 'I'm afraid because I'm naked,' he answers. 'I'm trying to hide from you.'

'You can't hide from me or yourself. You can't blame the woman because she gave you the fruit: you ate it, too! You can't undo what you did or pretend it didn't happen. You shouldn't have known good and bad. But now that you do, there are bad things in your lives and the world has changed.'

The man turns to the woman. 'We are still one. I'll call you Eve, giver of life. It will all be different now but we'll still be together.'

Adam is every man. Eve is every woman. They must leave their beautiful garden. They must work hard for food and sometimes feel sadness and pain.

They wander forever, remembering the beautiful life that is now a dream. God's image is still in them and God's blessing goes with them. They work for a perfect world, longing for the garden again. Everything beautiful reminds them of that perfect place and their hope for a good life is reborn.

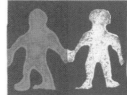

13

NOTES

The Hindu tradition is thousands of years old and one of the oldest religions in the world. Some say that it is not really one religion but several religions which are similar. Hindu beliefs and ways of life developed in and near India.

Many Hindu stories were handed down by word of mouth for thousands of years before they were written down. There are many Hindu stories about the beginnings of life. Each family and community tells the stories which they know and love best. Some of these stories are almost the same with just a few details that are different.

Hindus believe that each of us is both soul and body. Our bodies die but our souls live for ever. There is a Hindu saying: 'Smaller than the smallest, greater than the greatest, this Self forever dwells within the hearts of all.'

Hindus do not believe that the world was actually created in the way the stories tell; but the stories help people to feel how wonderful and mysterious creation is.

When the body dies, the soul enters another body. It is like an actor who takes on many parts, with different costumes and make-up. The soul passes through all forms of life, from insect to god. These forms of life are equally important because the Supreme Spirit is present in all of them.

HINDUISM

Making and Mixing

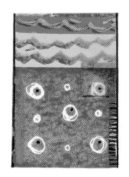

There is so much growing on the ground and so many creatures living on it – and yet the earth seems quiet and still. How can that be? Some say it is because Vishnu, the Supreme God, is asleep. But how could Vishnu be asleep?

Vishnu creates a cloud and a great ocean in its shadow, and lies down to sleep in the cool water, breathing deeply and evenly. Ages pass. Vishnu's energy creates a chain reaction that brings everything to life – all our senses and everything that we sense.

The sense of hearing... the sense of touch...
the sense of sight... The sense of taste...
The sense of smell...
Air and atmosphere...
Earth and water... Textures and forms...
Light and sound... Flavour and odour...
Everything in creation is joined – all our senses and all the element.

Vishnu blows clouds of tiny bubbles into the waters, and every time he breathes in they are sucked back inside him. Each bubble grows into an entire universe. All these universes cluster round Vishnu, like foam in the ocean.

For Hindus, there is one Supreme Being called Brahman, behind and within everything. Brahman takes many forms, is known by many names and plays many parts - just as people might have different names in different places, might be seen in different ways by different people and might behave differently in different situations.

'Everywhere are his hands and legs,
His eyes, heads and faces.
His ears are everywhere.
He knows all things,
past, present and future.
He knows all beings but
no one knows him.'
(from the Bhagavad Gita)

For many Hindus, Brahman acts in three main ways – creating… preserving, protecting and recreating… and destroying… There are three parts to Brahman. Brahma creates, Vishnu protects and Shiva destroys in order to create again. In some stories, such as this one, Vishnu creates the world; in some stories, such as *The Water, the Egg and the Fish* on the next page, Brahma creates the world.

'I am the original fragrance of the earth. I am the taste in water. I am the heat in fire and the sound in space. I am the light of the sun and the moon and the life of all that lives.'
(from the Bhagavad Gita)

Vishnu fills each universe with souls from his own nature. Souls needs bodies to enjoy the world so from Vishnu, Brahma is born. Brahma creates the planets, stars and gods. Brahma and the gods create the many forms of life in the universe, including humans. Oceans are Vishnu's waist, hills and mountains are his bones, clouds are hair on his head, air is his breath, rivers are his veins, trees are hairs on his body, sun and moon are his eyes and the passage of day and night is the moving of his eyelids.

Then Vishnu enters everyone's heart. Imagine two birds on the branch of a tree – one eating its sweet and bitter fruits, the other watching and waiting for it to turn. But the eating bird does not know the watching bird is there. The tree is like our body. The fruits of the tree are like our pleasures and pains. The eating bird is like our soul that has pleasure and pain. And the watching bird is like Vishnu who watches us all the time.

Vishnu is outside the world and inside the world at the same time. Vishnu is not really asleep in the ocean of creation but we are asleep because we are not aware of Vishnu! No one knows Vishnu but Vishnu knows everyone. Everything comes from Vishnu and returns to Vishnu.

NOTES

Many Hindus say that the world was not really created in the way that people cook or sew or construct a model, where they are separate from what they are making. It is much more like painting a picture, composing a song or performing a dance where, in a way, the thing which is created comes from inside the person who is creating it. It is more helpful to think that the universe emerges from the Supreme Spirit. A well-known Hindu writing says this is like a spider that makes its web from itself… or plants that grow out of the earth… or hair that comes from the body.

All Hindu creation stories show that everyone and everything is part of creation. We should live in harmony with nature and treat living beings with respect and kindness because the Supreme Spirit is present in them. Most Hindus do not eat fish or meat.

Not all creatures lay eggs like birds; but every living being, including humans, comes from an egg or a seed. That is why, for Hindus and many others, the egg is a symbol of life itself.

HINDUISM

The Water, the Egg and the Fish

There has always been a Supreme Spirit in the universe that exists by itself. Time came when the Spirit wanted living beings to form and grow. First came the waters. Then a seed ripened in them and from it grew a golden egg, as bright as the sun.

Some say that the Spirit developed within the egg as Brahma... Some say that the Spirit brooded over the egg as it lay on the surface of the ocean for a thousand years. Then a lotus flower, as bright as a thousand suns, rose from the navel of the Spirit and spread until it seemed as if it was big enough to have the whole world within it. From this lotus sprang Brahma, with all the powers of the Spirit of the universe.

Everything comes from Brahma. From Brahma's head rose the sky, from Brahma's navel the air, from Brahma's feet the earth, from Brahma's mind sprang the moon, from Brahma's eye the sun...

Some say that after a year in the egg, Brahma divided his body into two parts, male and female. The male joined with the female and Manu was born to create the world. Many ages came and went and after each one there was a new age. Perhaps every age has a Manu... perhaps each Manu is the same, escaping destruction and appearing over and over again.

The egg story has many variations, showing how the egg gave birth to part of the world. In one story, when the egg split into two, one became silver and the other gold. The silver one is the earth. The golden one is the sky. The outer membrane is the mountains. The inner membrane is cloud and mist. The veins are rivers. The fluid is oceans.

In other stories, parts of the world came from parts of the body of the first being. In one story, the head, arms, legs and feet became the four main groups in Hindu society: priests, warriors, farmers and traders, and labourers.

Throughout the world, there are ancient stories of floods that threaten to destroy everything, but some good or wise people are saved by building a boat and survive to start society again. The Manu story is one of the oldest.

Hindus use water in worship as a symbol of purity and refreshment. Water is like life in many ways: both can take different forms. Life appears in people, plants, insects. Water appears as ice, snow, hailstones, steam, droplets… life has ups and downs, like waves… life is wide, deep and mysterious like the sea… we cannot control life just as we cannot make water stop or run upwards…

One day, as Manu sat beside a stream, he heard a fish calling him. 'Help!' it cried. 'I'm being chased by another fish and I'm scared for my life. Please save me!' Manu gently lifted the fish out and put it in a jar of water. But the fish grew too big for the jar. 'Please take me to the Ganges where there's more room,' it begged. So Manu carried the jar and carefully tipped it into the river. The fish swam about freely but soon outgrew the Ganges, too. This time Manu took it to the ocean. There the fish was happy.

Then a strange thing happened. 'I am really Brahma!' the fish told Manu. 'You and all living beings are in grave danger and must save yourselves. Soon there'll be heavy rains and a flood will cover the whole world, destroying every living thing. Build a boat, and take into it seven wise people and the seeds of every living thing.'

Manu did this – and the flood began. The waters rose higher and higher, covering the earth. With strong cords joined to its horns, the fish pulled the boat across the water. It tossed about on the waves but everything inside was safe. It stopped on the top of the Himalaya mountains and Manu tied it to a tree. After many years, as the waters went down, the boat slowly descended into the valley. Manu and the wise people came out, bringing the seeds. There Manu began creating a new age in a new world, and another generation was born.

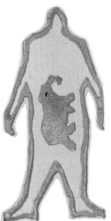

NOTES

There are many wise and fascinating Buddhist stories which help people to understand life and live better but there are no Buddhist stories about creation.

Buddhists believe that everything depends on something else and that something else depends on another something else... This goes on and on forever and the universe has no beginning or end. Many scientists today have similar ideas.

These two stories show that it is important to live and think well, and pointless to ask questions that have no answers. The Buddha probably did not know the tortoise story but there is a written record of the story in India a few hundred years later. Buddhists told it to illustrate one of his teachings:

'How pleasant is the speech of the monk
Who does not use too many words
Who controls his speech
Who talks wisely
And who is simple and clear in expressing the Dhamma (the teaching of the Buddha).'

(from the *Dhammapada*, verse 363)

Flying High and Falling Low

Torry was curious even when she was still a baby tortoise. She wanted to know where leaves came from, and why they were green and what made them juicy or dry... and why tortoises walk slowly while other creatures run or swim or fly. She was forever pestering older tortoises with her questions.

Sometimes they gave her good answers that made sense to her but sometimes she thought they just said anything to give her an answer. And some questions they simply couldn't answer. But no matter what they said or didn't say, Torry kept on asking.

'Why don't you just come and play?' her friends would ask. 'Or you'll end up looking like a question mark!'

One day, as Torry was thinking about this and that, along came two geese. It didn't take long for Torry to enquire where they came from and how they lived! 'Would you like to see for yourself?' one goose asked. 'I'd love to!' said Torry. 'But how? I can only walk – and slowly at that!' she explained. 'Easy!' replied the other goose. 'But you'll have to keep your mouth shut – so no questions... OK, Torry? Grab the middle of this stick in your mouth, we'll grip each end with our beaks – and we'll fly!' So off they went.

The whole earth stretched out below. Torry had only ever seen the ground and a few insects from above. Now she could see big things from above, as well. A new world opened up for her and it was beyond her wildest dreams.

The Buddha was born Siddhartha Gautama, in India about 2500 years ago. He was brought up as a prince. But, as he grew up, he felt there must be more to life than luxury and he wanted to find out about the world for himself so he left the palace.

He saw a sick man, an old man, a dead man and a holy man who seemed so peaceful that Gautama thought he would live like him, to find real happiness. He stayed in a forest with five people who deliberately went without food and sleep. That made him ill and he realised it was not the way to find peace and wisdom.

He had something to eat and decided to meditate under a tree until he understood what causes suffering and how to end it. He entered a state of perfect joy and peace that Buddhists call 'Nirvana'. He understood the 'Four Noble Truths' about suffering. He was then the 'Buddha', the 'Enlightened One' – the one who is really awake.

Until he died, he taught people what he understood about life and the causes of suffering. Through his teaching and his own example, many people understood their experiences and found real happiness.

Where were they going, she wondered, how high were they flying, how long would the journey take, and how had this beautiful place come to be.

As they soared over the gates of a palace, set in the side of the mountain, she spotted below two children pointing up at her. They seemed to be laughing. She opened her mouth to speak… was she going to ask them a question or was she going to give them a piece of her mind? Who knows?

She lost her grip of the stick and her goose friends watched helplessly and in horror as she plummeted to the ground, turning and tumbling through the air, and gathering speed as she went. In less than a moment, she had crashed in the palace courtyard. She lay on the hard, tiled floor, her shell cracked in two and her body limp and still.

Hearing the commotion, the palace officials rushed to see what had happened but were too late. It was a sad, curious sight – a dead tortoise in a courtyard. They asked themselves and each other what could possibly have happened and how she came to be there. Each of them had their own answer and recounted the story in their own way.

Torry died never knowing that one day she would be famous far and wide, from Ethiopia to China. And that her story would be told to Buddhists in India and would help them to understand something very important about the teaching of the Buddha.

NOTES

THE FOUR NOBLE TRUTHS

Buddhists everywhere accept the Four Noble Truths that the Buddha taught. Here is a summary of them:

1. There is suffering in life.
2. Suffering comes from a desire or greed that is not satisfied.
3. We can end suffering.
4. Following the Eightfold Path leads to the end of suffering.

THE EIGHTFOLD PATH

The Eightfold Path is based on wisdom, kindness and fairness, and mental discipline. It is a practical guide to the end of suffering through a wise, helpful and thoughtful life.

Buddhists do not take the steps of the Eightfold Path in order or even one at a time, but try to live by all of them. They are like eight spokes on a wheel that are all equal and joined at the centre. The eight-spoked wheel has become a symbol for Buddhism.

The Buddha, the Monk and the Arrow

 When Malunkyaputta heard the Buddha teaching, he became one of the Buddha's followers and lived as a monk. Something else happened later that again changed the way Malunkyaputta saw life.

Like other monks, Malunkyaputta spent several hours a day in quiet, concentrated thought. One afternoon, when he rose from his meditation, his head was buzzing with ideas and questions. He was desperate for answers to calm his mind and so he went to see the Buddha.

'I've got a lot on my mind, Blessed One,' he began. 'I've been wondering whether the universe will last for ever or some day end… whether space goes on and on or just stops… whether the soul and the body are really the same or different… If you have the answers, just tell me. And if you don't know, then why don't you just say "I don't know"?'

'Malunkyaputta,' replied the Buddha calmly, 'did I ever say to you, "Be my follower and I will explain these things to you"?'

'Well, no…'

'And did you ever say to me, "I'll be your follower and then you'll explain them"?'

'Well, no…'

'And we're not saying that now, are we? Anyone who says, "I won't be a follower of the Buddha until he explains them", would die before they were explained.'

The story of Malunkyaputta is very well known to Buddhists. He was a monk who asked the Buddha five pairs of questions.

Buddhist monks follow Gautama Buddha's example of giving up possessions and depending on the gifts offered to them. They meditate and help others understand the teachings of the Buddha. They live simple lives with only eight basic belongings, and no luxuries. They eat only one main meal a day, before noon.

The Buddha was very practical. Once, he took some leaves in his hand and asked some monks who were his followers, 'Where are there more leaves – in my hand or in the whole forest?' They replied, 'There are hardly any leaves in your hand but lots of leaves in the forest!'

He explained, 'The leaves in my hand are like what I have told you and the leaves in the forest are like what I haven't told you. What I haven't said is more than what I have said! That's because I've only told you things that'll help you live a good and happy life. Everything else is just empty ideas that aren't certain and don't get us anywhere.'

Malunkyaputta could see that the Buddha was not going to answer his questions but then the Buddha had never promised those sorts of answers – and he had never really asked them before. Then the Buddha said something that made Malunkyaputta think that he had been asking the wrong questions all the time!

'If someone's been shot by a poisoned arrow,' the Buddha said, 'and is taken to have it removed, just imagine them saying, "I won't have this arrow taken out until I know what kind of person shot it... what their name is... whether they're tall, short or of average height... what colour their skin is... where they come from... what kind of bow, bowstring and arrow they used... what sorts of feathers the arrow had... what the arrow head was made of..."'

Put like that, it did seem ridiculous to Malunkyaputta! These would be really stupid questions to ask in a situation like that. The most important thing would be to get the arrow out!

'That person would die without the questions answered,' the Buddha concluded. 'It's the same with your questions, Malunkyaputta. Whatever ideas anyone has, there's still sadness and suffering in life – and a way to end them. That's what I've been trying to tell you. And the reason I don't answer your questions is that there's no point!'

Some time later Malunkyaputta asked the Buddha a practical question: to help him understand suffering and how it can be ended. And Malunkyaputta himself became a holy one, worthy of the respect that people gave him.

NOTES

Several verses in the Qur'an (the holy book of Islam) refer to creation. There is no single, continuous story and the actual order of creation is not what matters to Muslims. The most important thing is that Allah (God) creates and knows everything.

A collection of writings (called the Hadith) which contains sayings and customs of the Prophet Muhammad, gives the order of creation: the earth, mountains, trees and water, sky, stars and angels…

The language of the Qur'an is quite like poetry. A day is thought of simply as a long time. One verse of the Qur'an says that a day is like a thousand years; another verse says it is like fifty thousand years.

In English, Muslims use capital letters not only for Allah's name but also for words which refer to Allah, such as He, His, Who, All Merciful… This shows their respect for Allah and their belief that He is the One and Only God.

ISLAM

The One and Only God

 Allah is the One and Only God. Allah will live for ever. Allah has no wife and no children. Allah knows everything and can do anything. Allah made everything for a reason. There is nobody and nothing like Allah.

Allah created the earth and the heavens in six days. They were all joined, but then He parted them and raised the sky like a roof. He created the night and the day, and the sun and the moon that float in their own orbits, and made the sun, moon and stars obey His commands.

He spread the earth and laid down hills that would not quake or shift, and rivers that would help people find their way. He made the winds blow and sent down rain to make the plants grow and for people to drink. Allah provided everything that people might need. Everything that Allah created was good.

Allah told the angels, 'I'm going to put someone in charge of the world, to represent me on earth.' They protested, 'Why must you put someone there who'll do harm and cause violence when we sing your praises all the time?' Allah replied, 'Don't you think I know more than you!' And they said, 'It's true that we only know whatever You tell us because You are All Knowing and Wise.' So Allah shaped a person from clay and called him Adam. He breathed His spirit into him, and gave him sight and hearing, knowledge and understanding.

31

Muslims never make pictures or statues of Allah because He has no body. Islamic artists show praise of Allah in many ways, especially through geometric patterns which reflect the intricate design of creation; flowery, leafy patterns which suggest the beauty of Paradise; and calligraphy of Qur'anic verses.

Allah specially created angels, from divine light, to perform certain tasks. People are free to do good or not, and to worship Allah or not. Angels do not have free will and always obey and worship Allah. They can take any form but people can only see them if they appear as humans. The Angel Gabriel revealed the Qur'an to the Prophet Mohammed about 1400 years ago.

Allah also created jinn (sometimes called 'genies' in English) from fire. Iblis was one of the jinn. They are usually tempters but some Muslims say they are natural forces of the universe, neither good nor bad in themselves.

Islam began with Adam, and the Prophet Muhammad is the last Messenger of Allah. Before him, there were other Messengers, including Jesus and several Jewish teachers. The Qur'an contains many teachings which also appear in the Jewish and Christian Bibles.

Allah told the angels to bow down to Adam and they did. Iblis, however, was proud and jealous of Adam, and refused. 'You created Adam from clay but you created me from fire,' he said. 'I'm better than him!' Allah cursed Iblis and said, 'Get out!' Iblis became Adam's enemy – and the enemy of everyone descended from Adam.

Allah taught Adam the names of plants and animals and asked the angels if they could say the names but they could not. 'We only know what You have taught us,' they explained, 'for you are All Knowing and Wise.' Then Allah asked Adam to say the names and he did.

Allah asked Adam to live in Paradise and created Eve as a partner for Adam. From that first pair come all the men and women in the world. Allah said to Adam, 'Live with your wife in this beautiful garden. You can both eat any fruit except from this one tree. Don't go near it! And watch out for Iblis who's trying to deceive and destroy you!'

But Adam and Eve let Iblis tempt them to the tree. And Allah said, 'Now you'll fall from Paradise and live on earth for the rest of your life.' Adam and Eve were really sorry for what they had done but Allah, who is All Merciful, forgave them. 'I will give you and all people guidance throughout your lives. If you follow it, you will be happy and, when you die, you'll return to Paradise.'

NOTES

'Four Men and One Woman' is not found in the Qur'an or any of the main Islamic writings. It is a folk tale from Saudi Arabia where almost the entire population is Muslim. Saudi Arabia is a desert country and there are no woods or lions there. So the story probably came from another country originally.

Devout Muslims pray five times a day – after dawn and before sunrise; at noon; in the mid-afternoon; just after sunset; and later in the evening. This marks the pattern of their daily life and helps them to be aware of Allah whenever they are awake.

Muslims can pray anywhere, in the direction of the Ka'aba in Makka, Saudi Arabia. As well as offering set prayers, Muslims may add personal prayers.

Muslims must be in a pure condition when they pray and so they wash their face and head, hands and arms, and feet in a special way and in a certain order. The ground where they pray must be clean. That is why Muslims carry a prayer mat when they are travelling.

ISLAM

Four Men and One Woman

 A carpenter, a tailor, a jeweller and a student of the Qur'an were once travelling together and spent the night in a wood. As there were lions around, they agreed to take turns in keeping watch.

It was the carpenter's turn first. He was afraid he would become drowsy or get bored and fall asleep. So, in the moonlight, he found a piece of wood and began chipping away until he had carved a statue of a woman. He shook the tailor, saying, 'It's your turn now
to keep watch!'

The tailor thought the statue needed some clothes. From leaves and grass that he found on the ground, he made garments and dressed it in a complete outfit. Then he woke the jeweller to take over the watch.

The statue seemed rather plain to the jeweller. So he made a necklace, bracelet and earrings of small stones. Satisfied with his work, he got the student out of bed.

The student found the statue very beautiful but he felt sad. 'There's nothing left to make,' he thought, 'and anyway I don't have any skills like the carpenter, the tailor and the jeweller.'

Just before dawn, he washed, unrolled his prayer mat and offered morning prayers, adding a prayer of his own, 'Lord of the world, I cannot carve wood, sew clothes or make jewellery. But I beg You to turn this statue into a real woman.' The statue began to move and talk. It was a living woman.

35

The events of this story did not actually take place. It is a parable about creation and creativity. Its main idea is that Allah creates and gives life. Human beings only create from things that Allah has already made and they cannot give things life.

The story also has a moral meaning. The student of the Qur'an is very devout in his prayers. He is also humble and is the only one of the four men who realises that Allah can bring the statue to life. In the end, he receives a reward.

In this story, the men haggle over the woman as though she is an object that they can own. In Islam, men do not own women and a woman is free to marry or not to marry any man who wants her for his wife.

Muslims do not believe in magical powers. But they do believe that Allah is All Powerful. This story recalls Muslims' beliefs about creation, as taught in the Qur'an. In this story, Allah brings a woman to life from wood. In the Qur'an, Allah brings to Adam to life from clay.

When morning broke, the other three woke up and realised that the dead wood had become a woman; the leaves and grass had become a velvet robe; and the stones had become precious jewels. Each one said that the woman was his and they began to squabble.

'I started her!' exclaimed the carpenter. 'If it hadn't been for me, there wouldn't have been a statue at all!'

'But you left her naked!' accused the tailor. 'I was the one who clothed her.'

'And you left her looking very plain, tailor!' shouted the jeweller. 'I bedecked her with jewels that made her beautiful. And as for you, carpenter, you may have started her but I completed her!'

They went on and on arguing, getting angrier and ruder all the time and almost becoming violent. In the end, they decided to take the matter to court and let the judge decide. The judge listened intently to what had happened and thought carefully about what it meant. Finally, he pronounced his verdict.

'Carpenter, you carved the statue from a piece of dead wood. You, tailor, clothed it with leaves and grass. And you adorned it with stones, jeweller. These are important but it is the spirit that gives life. The woman would never be alive if the student of the Qur'an hadn't prayed to the Creator to breathe life into her. The woman is therefore his and you three can have no share in her.'

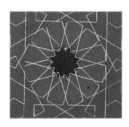

NOTES

Scientists work like detectives, searching for clues to solve a problem. They cannot just have ideas or beliefs of their own but try to find evidence to prove what happened. They do not always have all the facts and so they cannot prove absolutely everything. If that happens, scientists try to say what probably happens or happened. This is called a theory. The scientific theory in this 'story' is called the 'Big Bang'.

In other ways, the science 'story' is quite like other creation stories:

★

it is not an accurate account of what actually happened and there were no eye-witnesses;

★

not all scientists agree with this account and some have quite different explanations just as people have different ways of understanding traditional stories.

In some ways, this science 'story' is quite different from other creation stories:

★

the others are traditional tales that have been told for hundreds or thousands of years but the science 'story' is still being developed;

most traditional creation stories are ways of helping people to understand what life is all about and why things were created but scientific accounts try to piece together the facts of what happened and how the universe developed.

Stars and Space

The sky is so big that it is hard to imagine that what we can see is only a tiny part of a vast universe. At night, the stars in the sky seem very small but only because they are very far away.

Billions of years ago there was nothing but huge, empty space. Then there was an enormous explosion of energy and swirling clouds of white-hot gases were flung in all directions. Slowly, the gases began to cool and from them came galaxies of millions of stars and planets. Among these were our sun and the planet on which we live.

The stars and planets are not living. They do not eat and drink. They do not grow, move or change by themselves. They do not see, hear, touch, smell or taste. They have no life of their own. But another wonderful and mysterious thing happened that brought life to the planet Earth as it began to cool. Light from the sun gave energy. This energy, like electrical power, created thunderstorms that produced life from the gases.

Perhaps something like that happened to other planets in the universe. We do not know.

Scientists divide matter (physical things) into organic and inorganic. Organic matter is alive. Plants and animals are organic. They breathe, take food, reproduce, and die. Inorganic matter is not alive in this way.

'Organic' and 'inorganic' have nothing to do with size: both can be big or small. (For example, a flea and an elephant are organic; a mountain and a speck of dust are inorganic). Most scientists think that inorganic matter came before organic matter.

Plants and animals that died longest ago are in the lowest layers and those that died later must be in higher layers. So scientists can tell the order that they developed. One scientist says that studying fossil layers is like reading the story of the universe but some animals and plants are missing so there are 'gaps' in the fossil records – as if a page of the book of life is torn out.

When plants and animals long ago died, their bodies became rock. These 'rocky' plants and animals are called fossils. Rock has many layers, built up over millions of years. Scientists who study fossils can tell what these plants and animals were like. They have found different kinds of animals and plants in different layers of rock but animals and plants in any one layer are in the same layer everywhere.

The first life forms on Earth were very small and simple. There were probably some plants and animals then that are no longer in the world today. Others were perhaps like the tiniest of beings that we can still find today such as the bacteria that we know are all around us and that we all have in our bodies, even though we cannot see them with our eyes. Each of these small creatures probably only lived a very short time but they were able to reproduce, so life carried on.

As millions of years passed, other creatures began to appear on the Earth, bigger and more complex beings. The first lived in the water that covered the Earth. Then they moved to dry land where other beings began to develop.

There were…

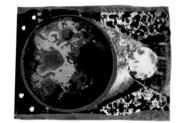

… seaweed, sponges, jellyfish and plankton…

… ferns, reeds and rushes…

… fungi, worms, snails and shellfish…

… shrubs and trees…

… insects and fish…

… trees and flowers…

… frogs and toads…

… snakes, lizards and dinosaurs…

… shrews and mice and rat… hamsters, gerbils and rabbits…

… cows, sheep, lions and horses, … monkeys and apes…

And all this time, there were tiny creatures too small to see with the human eye.

NOTES

Some traditional stories of creation say that every kind of creature there is now has existed ever since the universe was created. Individual creatures may grow or be born and die but that kind of creature goes on all the time and is the same as when it was first created. This kind of belief is called creationism.

Other traditional stories say that the kinds of creatures that exist now have been changing for a long time and are still changing and new kinds of creatures are developing ('evolving') all the time. This belief is called evolutionism. This 'story' is about the scientific theory of evolution.

Evolution is based on 'the survival of the fittest'. This does not mean that big, strong animals will survive and small, weak animals will be killed – or else there would be no small, weak animals alive today. It means that creatures that can fit in, or adapt, to their environment survive and those that can't die out. The same is also true of plants.

Cousins and Keepers

As time passed, life on Earth changed but not suddenly like someone dyeing their hair or getting bigger as they grow older. The kinds of creatures that existed on Earth changed very, very gradually. As each generation gave birth to another generation, the changes appeared in the newly born creatures.

Small plants or animals were perhaps blown about by strong winds or waves. Larger animals moved about to find food, water or a safer place to live. Some of those that did not move were all killed and that kind of creature died out. But even some of those that did move could not survive in their new home and they, too, died out.

Some creatures fitted in with their surroundings better than others. Perhaps a longer neck helped them eat leaves on tall trees… or the shape of their beak helped them eat the kinds of seeds and nuts growing there… Perhaps big ears helped them hear danger approaching… or good vision helped them see food from a long way off… Some creatures changed their habits to survive, like staying awake at night when they could hunt freely and without fear…

Those that fitted in well lived well. Later generations were born with bodies and habits like theirs – so they had a good chance of surviving, too. In this way, over many generations, millions of kinds of creatures changed.

43

Charles Darwin, a 19th century English Christian, is most famous for the theory of evolution but others had similar ideas before. He made a journey round the world, observing plants and animals in different environments. He brought back many samples of animals and plant life to look at closely.

Darwin noticed that creatures that survive are well adapted to their environment. When there are small differences in the environment between two spots, the creatures are different in small ways, too. Many scientists had been thinking that creatures evolve over many generations and what Darwin observed made them sure.

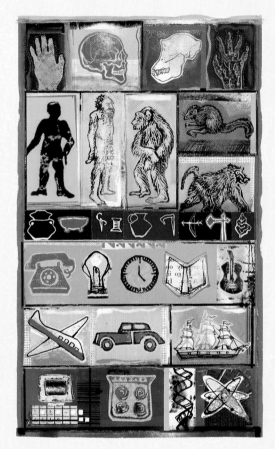

Some people also teased Darwin for saying that people are descended from monkeys. There were newspaper cartoons of people as animals in a zoo with apes as keepers. What Darwin did say was that monkeys and humans belong to the primate family and are both descended, in different ways, from primate ancestors.

Many Christians said Darwin was 'against' God. They thought he said everything happened by chance – without God designing and creating the world and being in control. Darwin always believed in God and said that evolution – like gradual creation – is the way God creates. Today, some Christians do not accept evolution and children in some American schools are not allowed to learn about evolution.

This happened to us, too. Humans and apes are the same kind of creature. Once, this huge family of animals that we belong to all lived in trees. Their tail and the shape of their arms and legs helped them move easily from branch to branch. About 4 million years ago, some of them started living on the ground and needed to walk upright. Our ancestors learned skills which helped them survive. Today, we still have many of those skills which make us unique.

For tens of thousands of years, people have used speech, music, drama and humour – not just sounds – to show what they think and feel. They have painted or written their ideas. They have created fire, used tools and made wheels. They have buried their dead.

In the last few thousand years, people have developed many kinds of tools and equipment – hammers, needles and spoons… carts, guitars and spinning wheels… and, in the last century, cars, televisions and computers… Many of these things help us live longer, more safely or in greater comfort. Every day, people are inventing or developing new technology.

Some people think that not all the change is good: many things we have made are spoiling the world and we are not in harmony with nature. Perhaps it is time for humans to change again and see the world's creatures as cousins in one big family. We humans have a special job: to look after the world and be its keepers.

45